The Big

Putting Pen to Paper

Bonkers

Doodah Book

Volume II

A Big Book By Small Children

First Published in Great Britain by Professional Marketing Limited, 1 Riseley Cottages, Selborne Road, Newton Valence, Alton, Hampshire GU34 3RN

Editor copyright © Sarah Lucas 2017.
Illustration & photography copyright © Putting Pen to Paper 2017.
The right of Sarah Lucas and Putting Pen to Paper to be identified as editor, illustrator and photographer of this work has been asserted by them in accordance with the Copyright, Designs and Patents Act 1988.

British Library Cataloguing in Publication Data.
A catalogue record for this book is available from the British Library.

ISBN 978-0-9557251-6-6
Printed and bound in Great Britain by Harmony Print.

madaboutsnailbooks.com

Visit http://www.madaboutsnailbooks.com/pen-to-paper-courses/ to read more about up-to-date courses and to view testimonials.
All illustrations have been designed by the children apart from above 'Friends' (page 115) and 'Dinosaurs' (page 140), published with grateful thanks to Microsoft (Word/ Clip Art/Library).

This BIG

Putting Pen to Paper

BONKERS Doodah

BOOK Volume II BELONGS to

....

Catamillamoth, the winning bottom-page design 2014/2015 by Erin South - and still looking pretty cool!

List of Contributing Authors, also known as 'the Small Children'

Milo Aulman *(aged 11)*
Ruby Aulman *(9)*
James Baldwin *(10)*
Amelia Barwick *(8)*
Lorien Boyes *(11)*
Naia Boyes *(9)*
Niall Cornelius *(9)*
Caity Cumner *(8)*
Ellie Cumner *(10)*
Finlay Denton *(8)*
Zoe Efstathiou *(10)*
Liv Fairhead *(11)*
Liam Fife *(11)*
Arlo Freer *(8)*
Wakely Ives *(8)*
Isobel Jewsbury *(9)*
Ingrid Linge *(9)*
Elodie Martin *(8)*

Eva McKell *(13)*
Orla Morrison *(9)*
Caitlin O'Boyle *(13)*
Maiya O'Boyle *(11)*
Joshua Panes *(7)*
Tom Panes *(7)*
Ben Parkes *(8)*
Jon Parr *(10)*
Robert Parr *(8)*
Daisy Redding *(10)*
Edward Scott *(7)*
Erin South *(9)*
Anna Styles *(8)*
William Twining *(11)*
Alison Weideman *(8)*
Caitlin Willcocks *(9)*
Katie Wood *(10)*

Katherine Baldwin *(8), new recruit;* Jemima Butler *(10), visiting illustrator*

NOTE: Ages are as at end of July 2016

Contents

Three **cheers** for:

- *Anna Styles*, whose figure at the bottom of the front cover was voted BEST DRAWING OF A BOY;
- *Eva McKell*, whose blurb on the back cover won BEST BLURB competition, and
- *Ruby Aulman*, whose winning design for the bottom inner pages, the fox, won BEST DRAWING FOR THE BOTTOM OF THE PAGE competition ...

... as voted by 'the small children'.

P_{utting} P_{en} to $P_{aper\ is}$ about ...

... *writing* ...

... it's about reading ...

... it's about being creative ...

... it's about expressing yourself.

*P*layful *Plots*

There are SEVEN basic plots. They are really very important because they help the author to order their story and help the reader to understand the chapters and order of the story they are reading. At Putting Pen to Paper we have been doing work on the seven plots because they help our writing to be more easily understood. You are probably wondering what the seven plots are. Well, they are: Overcoming the Monster, Rags to Riches, **The Quest**, Voyage and Return, Comedy, Tragedy and Rebirth.

Lorien Boyes

Well, we all know the story of Cinderella, don't we? It's a classic tale of Rags to Riches. What plot types are Lord of the Rings and Charlie and the Chocolate Factory? Some people, like Ruby, think there are not just seven but eight plots. Others think there are NINE. Here's what Ruby thinks ...

What About Horror?

HORROR isn't in the list, you say? Well, think again! HORROR gets you excited, nibbling your finger nails with worry. So why exclude it from the seven basic plots? There is no reason.

HORROR changes the fear factor. HORROR is freaky and interesting. SO WHY EXCLUDE IT? HORROR SHOULD BE A PLOT.

Ruby Aulman

What do you think? While you are mulling it over, here's a bit of comedy by Ben and Edward to tickle your funny bones.

Comedy Plot: Bob the Bankrupt

'One day I saw a microphone for £15,'
Bob Senior said to Bob Junior. 'I
bought it with all my money - now I am
bankrupt! So I sold the car for
£1,000. I sold the house for £9,000.
Now I've seen a guitar for £100,000
so I had to go and steal £90,000 from
the bank. I bought the guitar.

Now I'm bankrupt again but at least
now I am a popstar.' Luckily Bob Junior
never heard a word. He was deaf.
Life was good.

Story and illustration by Ben Parkes

Comedy Plot: Bang!

BANG!

They go to the moon.
Then they go to Mars

Then they hide. "Get down!"

It was a space buggy where
the aliens said they were
droids.

"Bang!"

"Get down! They'll see you."

The End

Cartoon and text by Edward Scott

Comedy Plot: Ginger and the Mouse

One snowy day a cat called Ginger was chasing a mouse through the jungle of curtain next to the world of window when he saw the bin man.

'Uh, ha,' said Ginger. 'The bin man.'
'Tickets please!' yelled the fat bin man.
'What's up with them?' thought Ginger.
'I know they're mad. This is a disaster.'
'Shut up!' yelled Ginger.
'What did you say?' said the bin man.
'I said: *shut up!* said Ginger.
'What?' said the bin man.
'Shut up!' yelled Ginger.
'Oh,' said the bin man.
Meanwhile the mouse disappeared.

Ben Parkes

Super Story Writing

Throughout this chapter you will experience stories like no other. With every story, excitement is carried. Bucket loads of fun will pour into your mind. These imaginative creations will carry you away.

Ruby Aulman

A Day in the Life of Spicy Radish Woman

Eat (yum). Sleep (zzz). Drink. Eat (yum). Sleep (zzz). Drink. Oh no, no, no! We can do better than that! My life is like any other person's but with big dips and hills of excitement .... ⌐⌐ ⌐⌐

Anyone can tell their life but not like me. I include expression and really I just tell it like I **enjoy** it. I have an exciting life in a short and stubby way. Would you like to hear about my life?

Tick the box ☐ YES ☐ NO

If you say **NO**, you shouldn't read on! And you have a real problem!

So, in the morning I have my breakfast which is normally salt and peppered **radish** with salty radish sauce. Then I go to Pilates to really warm up my radish powers. My five other friends, Prickly Parsnip, Terrible Turnip, Kicking Clementine, Boastful Banana and Pushy Pineapple come with me too, to warm up their powers. They are always so nice to me, so, so nice.

On Monday I went to my Super Men and Women Yoga. It is so easy and soon I will be moving up to

the next level. The next level is so high it is blue mat. After yoga I went for brunch with Kicking Clementine because I babysat her six children for three hours on Saturday night. Her kids are:

Jumping Juice (aged 12)

Plucking Peel (10)

Stupid Stork (6)

Skipping Skin (5)

Pomb Pomb Pip (3)

Silent Section (1).

At night I went down to the **Frightful** Fruit Bowl. We had so much fun watching the great entertainment. Our favourite entertainment was 'The Greens', a great band that comes every Friday.

To be continued ...

Lorien Boyes

Underwater Treasure

One day there was a boy named Finn who was going on holiday to the beach.

Eventually, Finn, his mum and dad arrived.

At the beach there were caves. Finn had heard that the caves were under water.

The next day, Finn put his diving gear on and headed down to the caves.

In the first cave he went into, he found a map! But suddenly he had to go back to his parents so he took the map with him. The next day he took his diving gear and headed back down to the cave. He got out the map, went underwater and suddenly saw a skeleton behind which there was treasure.

Illustration by Liam Fife

A shark came out of nowhere. Finn swam for his life. As soon as he got out of the cave, he ran for his life back to the hotel.

Finlay Denton

How my Story Begins …

It all started a while back now. I guess it has been a long time. Well, this is my story …

I was on a cold, draughty plane, the XX19, my private jet. I had a lot of money because I was The World's Greatest Vet, even though I was only thirteen. But I had already finished my degree!

The plane was about to land in Austria. I could see the set for The Sound of Music. They wanted me to come and watch them do their performance even though I was The World's Greatest Thirteen Year Old.

Illustration by Lorien Boyes

I got to help them perform. Then once the day was over, I left on the XX19. I was back home by nightfall.

Caitlin O'Boyle

Fang and Foltra

Fang is a wolf and Foltra is a fox. They are best friends and always play together. One day they fell out with each other and had a big fight. Their parents came running and stopped the fight. They made Fang and Foltra friends again and they never had another fight.

The End

Story and illustration by Wakely Ives

It all Started When ...

It all started when my dad ate the terrifying sprouts. I watched his bum wriggle. I screamed! His bum squeaked and I fainted. It came out. As I woke up, the family was choking on the fart.

Suddenly I heard, 'Help, my boy!'

I held in a fart and ran to the door but tripped and dropped my toy. To pick up the toy and to keep on reading, I ran away around the back. But when your dad arrives and shouts: 'I'm gonna blow!' slowly ... you drop down DEAD.

Arlo Freer

From Being Enemies to Becoming Friends

It all started in the playground at school. Caitlin, Elodie, Amelia and Caity had had a fall out and were being mean to one another about who had the highest score in the English test in class. Caitlin said, 'Well, I got full marks which is 100%.' 'Yeah, well I got 92% which is still quite good, isn't it?' questioned Elodie. 'Not as good as getting 100%,' Caitlin said nastily. 'I can't see why we can't all be friends,' said Caitlin sensibly. 'Well we never are going to be friends if we keep arguing, are we?' Amelia declared. That's what the rest of the children in the playground were trying to figure out, why they couldn't all be friends?

One night, Caity, Amelia, Elodie and Caitlin were all in bed and in their own houses when there came a terrible storm. The thunder rumbled like mad, then the sky turned dark grey, the rain hammered down making so much racket, none of the enemies could get a wink of sleep. Every now and then there came big flashes of lightning and every single one of the girls nearly jumped out of their skin, petrified.

It was then, that night, that they couldn't stand it a second longer. So shaking all over, they crept out of bed and out into the freezing cold weather. Each one of them stumbled into the forest where they stopped and stared at one another. Each one of them was thinking: 'What are *they* doing here?' Then Caity stepped forward and said: 'We need to think of a plan to catch the monster that is trying to keep us apart.'

'She's right,' Elodie agreed. They huddled together and thought of a plan. Finally they agreed and they set their plan into action. Elodie was holding a net ready to catch the monster, Amelia was ready to shout, 'Over here!' to beckon the monster closer so they could catch it. Caitlin put a rope reaching across two tree trunks so they could trip the monster up so Elodie could pull the net over the monster when it fell over the rope. Caity was going to tell everybody when to do their things.

Then they heard footsteps and the monster heard Amelia calling and was in such a hurry it tripped over the rope that Caitlin had set up. As soon as it fell to the ground Caity shouted, 'Now!' to Elodie who put the net over the monster. They jumped down from their places and took off the gigantic monster's mask to see who it was. To their surprise it was the school children from their class. 'But why?' Caitlin asked, astonished. 'We wanted you to be friends,' they said. 'Well I guess we can be friends, don't you agree everyone?' asked Amelia with hope.
'Yes we can!' chorused the girls.
So in the end all the enemies became friends.

Caitlin Willcocks, Elodie Martin, Amelia Barwick and Caity Cumner

Minecraft Madhouse

– Opening Chapter

I am Posy and my friends are Aivilo, Tay, Rufus, Parody, Moonlight, Heaven L … the list goes on and on and maybe … ON!!! We all have our personal talents even though we are all in the same group. If I told you who is best at what, I would be here all week. I think you could probably work it out if you have at least one brain cell … anyway, we kind of get on apart from when the Tamers, Tay and Rufus get into an argument with Parody, our combat chief. It's kind of like 'Redstone vs. Combat' when they are around.

We have our own groups inside the main group which makes no sense whatsoever but try telling Untamed that. I am best at crafting, enchanting, taming cats and dogs and making a complete fool of myself. The last one is not my fault. As my worst enemy is always on my back, trying to dispose of me and my lap dogs which, as you can tell, is a little bit annoying.

Anyway, I am waiting for Rufus to get his butt into gear and build our new base (we haven't got all night). As you can tell my brain is almost leaking out of my ears and solidifying on the floor hence I am now writing in this book (sorry, chew toy). Thanks, but no thanks, Wolfie. So I will try to write our story.

Okay, enough of my pointless yatter. Let's get on with it and, Rufus, if you are looking over my shoulder, then DON'T take your time building this thing because it's beginning to rain and I REALLY don't want to be soaked.

Liv Fairhead

The  Disease

One day there was a fart that polluted the air but everybody wanted to see it. Eventually they caught the farting disease. Dan, dan dar ...! So they all started farting.
They all wanted to see their farts but just made bigger farts. Eventually they could see their farts all about them. It was horrifying to see. They started fainting. It was *soooooo* cool.

Ben Parkes & Finlay Denton

Mutant Fish

Robert is doing a peaceful spot of fishing on a peaceful lake on a sunny day. He had two pike, one herring. He was after one more fish to finish his collection. He got it. It was a mutant fish! The fish escaped and flew towards the city.

Robert headed towards the other side of the world. Suddenly, his car got caught by seaweed. He pushed the pedal down but it did nothing. He got sucked back.

Robert thought of the only way to catch him. 'Yum! Think how many fish fingers I can make with that! But I don't want to mess with him.'

Robert went back to his fishing unaware that only one fish was there ...

James Baldwin & Robert Parr

We found a fish puppet on the floor – can you see it above? - and this inspired us to write the story, 'Mutant Fish'.

Something Can be Different in Friendship

Lucy thought everything about her was nothing different to anyone else. Until she saw a giant painted finger wherever she went and every time they were different coloured fingers.

She thought that she would go into the kitchen to have a snack before tea. Her Dad was in there with a high vis yellow jacket on which stated on the back 'FIRE MARSHAL'. She didn't think much about it then but one week later ...

She met Shade, her new friend who was trying to investigate the crime as well. But when they found a bomb in her Dad's office, a blind onion bomb, Shade touched it so now he was going to be accused.

The next day Lucy went to the kitchen and her Dad appeared once more in the jacket, glasses and a moustache. At the same time she got a text from Shade to say that he had been arrested.

Caitlin O'Boyle

This piece of writing was inspired by 'The Prop Game', a game where each group is given a black sack with weird things inside – like a pair of glasses, an onion, a yellow high-visibility jacket – and the group has to make up a story using the props.

The No-name Orphan

I am an orphan with no name, raised in the jungle by myself. I live in a tree in the canopy. This is my story.

I was one when I was abandoned like a cockroach in a house, thrown out and abandoned. I learnt to live and survive by observing how the animals lived, eventually making friends of them. I lived a happy life.

Once I heard news of the loggers I was astonished that someone would do such a thing. So I set out to stop them.

First I tried to persuade the local tribesmen to stop fighting and go against the great evil of the loggers reducing our home by the minute. Some agreed, others did not.

We crossed the river using their bridge to help us, storming the camp, we sabotaged the equipment and polluted the water supply. There was to be no bloodshed. I forbade it.

In the morning we awoke to the anguished cries of the loggers. They were annoyed their machinery wouldn't work. Vad (my friend) was surveying them, enjoying their discomfort. We had won.

But we had only won a minor battle - the loggers could buy more machinery, we needed to dispose of them and get rid of them completely so they would never come back – the question was "how?".

Eventually we formulated a plan – distract the loggers and cut out food and water supplies completely, get rid of the cars and trucks and wreck their cabins so they would never be able to live in them again.

A month later the loggers were gone. All that remained were a few tree stumps burned, torched and blackened.

Milo Aulman

THE GREATEST GUINEA PIG EVER

by William Twining

Bertha was big. Everything about her was big. Big head, big feet, big legs, big arms, big hands, big fingers, big stomach and even a big bum. She was definitely big. Also she had big but mean ambitions to capture guinea pigs and keep them in cruel captivity. But, the biggest thing she has is laziness. She yells at her troop of men to do everything for her. Capture guinea pigs. Feed her. Clean her. Think for her. And even pick her toenails for her! Revolting! That's Bertha for you!

Underground was a school full of guinea pigs. Teaching Guinea Pig Primary, was a rather miniature guinea pig – Mrs Whiskers. Unluckily for her, she has a class of ten mischievous students: Jett who loves running. During every lesson he starts sprinting around the classroom. Scrabbles who loves playing board games. In each class, he sits there playing games (his favourite is Scrabble! Surprise, surprise!). Squeaky Squeaky Squire screams at everything she sees. Once when the light was switched off, she screamed so loud that Mrs Whiskers had to go to the hospital to get her ears checked! Ginger loves eating biscuits. When he spotted a pack of biscuits by the teacher, he snuck up and gobbled them all

unnoticed! Popping Icepop can't keep stationary for five seconds. One time she was left alone for one minute, and turned everything completely upside down! Nibby eats everything he sees. Once he ate the teacher's chair, and when she sat down, she fell right on the floor! Sugarpop Star adores singing. When she becomes bored in lessons, she begins to sing ten green guinea pigs! Mittens is always frozen. When everybody was wearing summer clothes, she had two coats on and five layers underneath! Sociable never stops talking. He always chats to Mittens who is next to him, but he never receives a reply! The tenth guinea pig is George, who just sits listening to the teacher.

On one ordinary school day, something unusual happened. Nibby was extra hungry this day and decided that he needed to find food. At lunchtime, he sneaked out of school and beyond the undergrowth.

After a few hours, he reached an enormous house. Written on the centre of the huge doors, were the initials 'BB`. Unaware of the dangers he might face, Nibby opened the doors...

Right before him stood a colossal table with a vast variety of glorious food on top of it. Unfortunately for Nibby, he couldn't see that. He crawled towards the table, sniffing eagerly. Crunching on the table legs, he didn't realize that the plates were gradually slipping off the table.

CRASH! Crockery and cutlery smashed into a hundred pieces. Suddenly, a booming voice echoed around the room. "Who goes there?" Petrifaction plunged through poor Nibby like a burrowing fox. Squeaking in terror, he ran as fast as his tiny legs could carry him. Through the doors he went, and arrived in the open land. Not daring to take a glance back, the frightened guinea pig was desperate to return underground. In the distance he could see the hole he exited from. Almost there, he thought. Survival was what he craved as he neared his destination...

Although he was now in safety, Nibby was still sprinting underground. He careered round the corner, and

entered the route to a collision course with... Mrs Whiskers!

Back in her mansion, Big Bertha was yelling at her troop for being lazy and failing to capture the escapist. Thinking exactly the same thing, everybody stared at her *massive stomach, but not a single mouth opened. Anger got the better of her as she released her fury.*

"Ya useless idiots!"
"Ya ridiculous runts!"
"Ya no good losers!"
"Ya stupid slugs!"
"Ya pathetic pigs!"
Fuming, she slapped each soldier twice on the cheek and stormed away, causing every table to shake.

Down underground, Mrs Whiskers was giving poor old Nibby a real spanking. Afterwards, she was about to finish the punishment when ...

Concrete crumbled down on the class, producing a whole lot of dust, which made the students cough. The dust began to vanish, revealing ten tall soldiers armed with spades. They were about to harm the class of guinea pigs when a pair of big feet appeared. Then big legs. Then big thighs. Then a big bum. Then a muffled voice saying: "Help me! I'm stuck." The troop tugged and tugged and tugged and tugged until ...

THUD!

There appeared Bertha, mean and ugly as normal. Her landing caused all of the guinea pigs to topple over like dominos, except for George, who stayed on his feet. She started to cackle at the trembling class. Then deafening screeches drowned Bertha's laughing.

"She's going to capture us!" shouted Jett.

"She's going to torture us!" wailed Ginger.

"We're going to die!" squeaked Squeaky Squeaky Squire.

"She's going to squash us with her belly!" screamed Sugarpop Star.

"She's going to flatten us with her bum!" cried Sociable.

"She's going to make an earthquake!" sobbed Popping Icepop.

"My games have gone," panicked Scrabbles.

"I'm cold," moaned Mittens.

Petrified, everyone darted away, abandoning George. Although alone, he was defiant. Instantaneously, Big Bertha reacted. Aiming to hurt George, her punch was hurtling straight at him at terrifying speed. He was bound to get squashed.

Her fist was jammed in to the ground. "I'm stuck!" she called. Dropping their spades, the soldiers trudged over to help her. An idea popped into George's head.

Stealthily, he sneaked around and took hold of a spade. Dragging it along the floor, he came face to face with Big Bertha. Guinea pig against human. Who will overcome their enemy and be victorious? With all the might he contained, George smacked the spade right at her face. Immediately, she was in concussion – hopefully for a long period of time.

The task was not yet complete. The troop stomped menacingly towards George. Never in a million years would a guinea pig defeat ten men...

Suddenly, something peculiar happened. Instead of trying to kill George, they began to thank him and become friends. An explanation was given by one of the soldiers. "We never liked Big Bertha anyway. She was absolutely horrible. Thanks."

But George had one more thing to do. "Guys," he shouted, "I've defeated our enemy and have made new friends."

And that is the story of the greatest guinea pig ever.

William Twining

MURDER Secret

There once were two friends, Evie, who was a liar, and Emily, who was stupid. Emily accidentally punched someone in the face and the person died. That is where the story begins.

Quickly, they ran before the Police found out. It was deep and dark in the forest and at one point they both fell over at the same time. When they got home they struggled to act calm. Evie ruined the whole secret by saying: 'We did not just kill someone in the forest.' Luckily her mum didn't believe her.

Emily was stupid and of course she told the Police the story. Then Evie and Emily ended up in jail.

Amelia Barwick

*R*idiculous Robots

Illustration by William Twining

Open the door into a robotical world of wonder. Let new inventions and flying cars take your breath away. Just imagine it, a chapter of children's creations. Read on and find new evolutions of ideas. Read on …

Ruby Aulman

MedusI, *by Liam Fife*

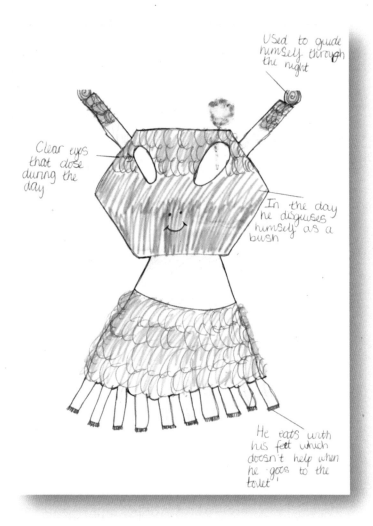

Used to guide himself through the night

Clear eyes that close during the day

In the day he disguises himself as a bush

He eats with his feet which doesn't help when he goes to the toilet!

BUSHBOT, *by Caitlin O'Boyle*

BLOB JUNIOR, *by Jemima Butler & Naia Boyes*

GROBLET, *by Katherine Baldwin*

BLOBERINA, *an interpretation of the original BLOBERINA by Naia Boyes*

BLOBERINA MEETS SCI-FI

(Writing prompt): **An asteroid is heading for Earth. From their planet, the aliens are watching. Bloberina stops dancing to watch ...**

Swatty Spotty watches in excitement. The Comet has jet legs and with green lime jelly.

Blob said "Swatty Spotty, the Comet is fast."

Suddenly the Comet turned round and went straight for Mars. The aliens were shocked: "Swatty Spotty Ot Ow". The Comet turned again to Pluto, the dwarf planet. It destroyed Pluto "Ot Ow" then went straight to Neptune. Swatty Spotty jumped onto the Comet.

Edward Scott

Spectacular

Sci-fi Meets Cool Christmas

Like science? Like stories? Spectacular Sci-fi could be for you. This section is exploding with tense scriptwriting which steals your breath, and made-up monsters full of creativity. With writing prompts to help imagination, this writing is erupting with creations. Literally.

William Twining

Scriptwriting: The Meteor Fight

An asteroid is heading for Earth. From their planets, the aliens are watching. Blob Junior, one such alien, stops dancing to watch.

> BLOB JR.
> What is that?

BLOB JR. points at a meteorite. The crowd gasps.
While GROBLET looks, BLOB JR. kicks him

> GROBLET
> Here, have a drink.

GROBLET shoots lava. BLOB JR. screams. Both punch, slap and kick each other for a minute.

> BLOB JR.
> That's enough.

BLOB JR. tries to hypnotise GROBLET as GROBLET reflects the eye back. BLOB JR. punches himself to death.

GROBLET
Ha! Never underestimate the power of
the …

The meteorite lands on GROBLET.

Lesson from the story: never reflect a hypnotising eye at your opponent when a meteorite is flying directly at your face. It will most likely NOT help you in life. ☹

James Baldwin & Jon Parr

NOTE: *The layout of this scriptwriting exercise was based on the original screenplay script of The Lord of the Rings, The Fellowship of the Ring by Fran Walsh, Philippa Boyens and Peter Jackson which in turn was based on the book by J.R.R. Tolkien.*

WRITING PROMPTS

(Writing Prompt): A Sci-Fi Adventure Happened on the way to Putting Pen to Paper ... *so there I was, day-dreaming, my thoughts GALAXIES away, staring into space when ... Whoosh! Zoom! Whizzo! I really WAS staring into SPACE – The Final Frontier! Right before my Sci-Fi eyes was a brand new PLANET. I can only describe it as ...*

... beautiful, luscious and swimming with life.

It was the most extra-ordinary thing I had seen that LIGHT YEAR! I had to get to Pen to Paper and write it down faster than the SPEED OF LIGHT. But as I ran out of the house I fell into a WORM-HOLE and TIME TRAVELLED to the year ...

... 2100 AD when people were coming around on hover boards and the telephone boxes made you teleport to where the person was you wanted to talk to.

'BEAM ME UP! BEAM ME UP!' I shrieked, but my words were sucked into a VORTEX. No-one could hear me. I was stuck on this

planet and in this year, my only hope was rescue by a passing ...

... boy who was my son's-son's, son reoccurring ... and his name was Galacticus and he was meant to be named after me.

I stared at the non-human in front of me. My eyes were as wide as FLYING SAUCERS. The non-humans' eyes were ...

... glowing green and reacting to his body making it glow in a lime-flavoured jelly kind of way. I screamed as I noticed a suction cup on his head, the mind-making species of brains.

It picked up a LIGHT SABER and wrote a message in the SPACE DUST. The message said: hero – villain – extinction – last MINDMASTER.

'Well,' I decided, 'there's only one thing for it!' I reached into my SPACE CADET rucksack and pulled out my ...

... alien infoductor and typed in
MINDMASTER and it popped up exactly as
they boy had encrypted.

*As if an ASTEROID had exploded, my mind
bulked up with facts ...*

... the blurbs were dominators but they died out
and this was the only remains of organic life
forms from different universes.

James Baldwin

**A Sci-Fi Adventure Happened on the
way to Putting Pen to Paper ...** *so there
I was, day-dreaming, my thoughts
GALAXIES away, staring into space when
... Whoosh! Zoom! Whizzo! I really WAS
staring into SPACE – The Final Frontier!
Right before my Sci-Fi eyes was a brand
new PLANET. I can only describe it as ...*

... a cube. I then thought of a name for it:
Cubonia. There was a volcano spitting out lava
but I wasn't scared. I had to be the first person
to land on it! I hoped nobody had named it
something different. Finally, there was a

ninth planet. As soon as I saw it, I knew it definitely would not be a dwarf planet. I hoped I could meet an alien when I went.

It was the most extra-ordinary thing I had seen that LIGHT YEAR! I had to get to Pen to Paper and write it down faster than the SPEED OF LIGHT. But as I ran out of the house I fell into a WORM-HOLE and TIME TRAVELLED to the year ...

... 1950. Luckily my friends, Sophie and Caity fell down with me! We ended up getting trained to do housework which I hated.

'BEAM ME UP! BEAM ME UP!' I shrieked, but my words were sucked into a VORTEX. No-one could hear me. We were stuck on this planet and in this year, our only hope was rescue by a passing ...

... satellite. We could run into a TV and get back home in 2015. I wrote what happened in my Putting Pen to Paper book. When I got home an alien had followed me.

Illustration by Naia Boyes

I stared at the non-human in front of me. My eyes were as wide as FLYING SAUCERS. The non-humans' eyes were ...

... just a huge iris. I ran up to my bedroom and hid under my bed. I heard the alien say, 'Hello. I want to be your friend!'

It picked up a LIGHT SABER and wrote a message in the SPACE DUST. The message said ...

... come to Cubonia and live with me. I stared at the message. I said, 'Of course!' because my parents never looked after me.

'Well,' I decided, 'there's only one thing for it!' I reached into my SPACE CADET rucksack and pulled out my ...

... onion and cut it into pieces. I started to cry then fed it to the alien. The alien said, 'I like onions.' So I gave him more.

Illustration by James Baldwin

It was as if an ASTEROID had exploded. As the SPACE DUST finally settled all the alien could **say** *was ...*

'I am leaving. Come with me now.' So I did. We travelled. I never set foot on Earth again. There was no gravity on Cubonia so I had SO much fun.

Amelia Barwick

A Sci-Fi Adventure Happened on the way to Putting Pen to Paper

... so there I was, day-dreaming, my thoughts GALAXIES away, staring into space when ... Whoosh! Zoom! Whizzo! I really WAS staring into SPACE – The Final Frontier! Right before my Sci-Fi eyes was a brand new PLANET. I can only describe it as ...

... an alien mountain, huge, red and round.

It was the most extra-ordinary thing I had seen that LIGHT YEAR! I had to get to Pen to Paper and write it down faster than the SPEED OF LIGHT. But as I ran out of the house I fell into a WORM-HOLE and TIME TRAVELLED to the year ...

... 2004. Luckily I got out quickly because I wasn't born in 2004 and it could be crazy.

'BEAM ME UP! BEAM ME UP!' I shrieked, but my words were sucked into a VORTEX. No-one could hear me. I was stuck on this planet and in this year, my only hope was rescue by a passing ...

... person or animal to pull me out of the vortex.

I stared at the non-human in front of me. My eyes were as wide as FLYING SAUCERS. The non-humans' eyes were ...

... the same as mine. Then I saw the clock had changed to 2014 when I was alive. I found out the people had made me and I bumped into myself.

It picked up a LIGHT SABER and wrote a message in the SPACE DUST. The message said ...

... Who are you?

'Well,' I decided, 'there's only one thing for it.' I reached into my SPACE CADET rucksack and pulled out my ...

... sword and chopped off his head.

It was as if an ASTEROID had exploded. As the SPACE DUST finally settled, all I could see was ...

... I HAD KILLED MYSELF.

Robert Parr

Ghastly

Gruesome

Murder

Writing

In these murder stories, you will find gruesome deaths and fabulous killers. I know that doesn't sound right but, you know, no-one cares. Anyway, let's move on. As you flick through the pages of these stories, remember to bring a friend to huddle with.

Anna Styles

The Cereal Killer

One morning a boy woke up and went down the stairs to have breakfast. The thing he had for breakfast was cereal. He took one spoonful and ate it. One minute later he was coughing and choking. That morning he died.

Naia Boyes

Illustration by Jon Parr

Death is Not Fun

I pulled the hood over my head and patted my jacket. There was a reassuring lump in my pocket: I sighed in relief. I nervously glanced around at the deserted field for the hundredth time that day. I was alone.

Swiftly, I turned and quick-walked into the shadow of trees.

Once I was out of sight from other people, I broke into a run, racing through the forest. I jumped over the fallen trees and ducked under low branches. Suddenly I stopped. I unzipped my pocket and produced a sharp knife. I ran a finger along the edge. Blood dripped from my hand. I grinned. Slowly I walked up to a pair of huge, iron gates. I jumped and grabbed the gate, then pushed up with my feet. When I reached the top, I let myself drop to the floor, landing with a bang! A large, three-storey house stood before me. I shuddered in fear. I nervously walked up to the front door and knocked. A man stepped out. My knife stabbed him.

Eva McKell

Ouch!

by Caitlin O'Boyle

Lily was standing by the side of the road, waiting for her mum to pick her up from Goth

Club, She was wearing all black and looking at her feet all the time.

Feeling the breeze in her hair and hugging her tummy, even though the sun was at full beam, she felt a shiver go up her spine as a man crept up behind her. He was wearing all black. That was all she could see from the blur.

He pulled a knife out of his pocket. With one stroke of a knife's blade, Lily's head was off the neck and on the floor.

Her mum then pulled up to find Lily's dad with a knife in his hand.

Caitlin O'Boyle

Triangular Roof

PROLOGUE

I have found a way. A way to KILL Triangular
Roof ONCE AND FOR ALL.

Chapter One

Hello, my name is Triangular Roof. Don't ask
about my name, it's a long story. I used to
own one of the most famous wolf packs. I
still remember their names: Zippy, G. Paws,
namely, Nancy, Norris, Tikki and Fangs. The
one who started it all. Okay, maybe it's time
to explain ... there is a guy ... a guy
called ToDecks. Anyway, ToDecks ('Decks') is
evil. He wants to kill me. Why? I'm not sure
why. I think it's an old family rivalry. Oh
yeah! My family, my life ... I live in a
house on an island in the middle of the sea.
I would give you the details but I'm not sure
if I can trust you yet. You might be another

of Deck's clones. But if Deck EVER got hold of
this ... it's info. he knows already ...

I think I can trust you. I could show you a
picture of me drawn by my sidekick, Spawn ..
but then again?

Wolf Central is basically a section of the
sea dedicated to wolves. 'Why?' you ask.
Because it's a place where half-human wolves
can develop wolf packs and live like wolves
in peace. I'll show you Deck. He can rip
people's heads off. He already killed half my
wolf pack.

Chapter Two

I feel like I am being watched ... WAIT!
Please save me ... I did it ... I ... I
killed him. I killed Deck by accident. Oh no!
I a-m d-y-i-n-g ... he ... he poisoned me.
RID: Rest in Discomfort, Deck. RIP Triangular
Roof.

Liv Fairhead

*M*agnificent
Mystery Writing

In Volume I of the Bonkers Book we had a crime about stealing the Bonker's Board. This is another crime scene, as written by Eva. Keep your eyes peeled to see if any criminals are around. **WATCH OUT!**

Naia Boyes

Mystery Writing: A(nother) Crime Scene

On 13th May 2016, a mysterious note was discovered on one of the chairs at the Alton Maltings while Putting Pen 2 Paper was holding a course. Three people have been arrested and are awaiting trial.

Eva, Sarah and Olivia were the first people in the room. It was a few minutes later when Caitlin discovered the secret note laying on her chair. After an hour of investigating, the children finally arrested Eva, Sarah and Olivia on suspicion of planting the suspicious note. Kate (a helper) said:

'I believe it was Eva. She was first in, so had enough time to plant the note. She also looked very suspicious.'

Caitlin (aged 13) explained how Olivia's handwriting matched that on the note. We interviewed the suspects but they all refused to talk. In two weeks we will finally know who planted the note. I personally believe it was Sarah with her similar handwriting and because she is an adult.

Eva McKell, Crime Reporter

Treacherous

Time
Travelling

This chapter contains a series of treacherous stories about time travelling people who go on exciting journeys through tunnels that lead to new galaxies and unexplored planets. Come with us and experience new places.

Finlay Denton

IN FIVE SECONDS ...

(Writing Prompt): A white light flickered at the end of the tunnel. I put both hands before me and began to crawl. Wind kissed my cheek. A whirring noise grew in my ear. Something pulled me forward ...
What happened next?

In my ventilation pipe I could hear a noise counting down: 5... 4...3... going forward ... 2 going forward ...1. FIZZ! BANG! BOOM! I tripped forward and I stopped in the cretaceous period and the Tyrannasaurous Rex time. I came out in a pine forest and a terrible sight met my eyes: I was in a T-Rex battle ground and I was lunch.

Suddenly they started fighting each other. Here was my chance! I darted out of the forest but met an even bigger problem. At first I didn't see it. I saw a big object drifting towards Earth. It was a meteor. The victorious T-Rex started emerging from the battlefield closing in on me. I could be lunch then die, or not. I chose to dart to the teleporter, pressed 'RETURN', just as the asteroid hit. In five seconds I was back climbing out of my ventilation pipe. I was alive.

James Baldwin

CONFUSING STORY

A white light flickered at the end of the tunnel. I put both hands before me and began to crawl. Wind kissed my cheek. A whirring noise grew in my ear. Something pulled me forward ...

What happened next?

As I walked in this strange land I found a robot. It was very fat and blue. Then I saw someone surfing on nothing, just flying on the open sea. Then: KABOOM! I thought it was getting confusing. SHHHH-FAM! KLOOM! CREEEEEK! The world went KABOOM! 'What the heck is KABOOM?' I wondered.

Then I remembered I was dead so I must have been dreaming, but how can I when I am dead? Am I not *dead*?

Robert Parr

'KILL ME!'

A white light flickered at the end of the tunnel. I put both hands before me and began to crawl. Wind kissed my cheek. A whirring noise grew in my ear. Something pulled me forward

... What happened next?

Suddenly I saw **me** coming from the other end of the tunnel. How could this work? Was it **me** from the future? The future-me looked into my eyes. 'I know what's going on!' she told me, 'I am future-you, coming back from where you're going now!' It was impossible for me to get through the tunnel as the future-me was blocking my way. But then I figured it out: if future-me killed me, then that would be a paradox but I could survive in the paradox as I would not be in the time tunnel. 'Kill me!' I said to the future-me. 'What?' she shouted back. 'Cause a paradox!' I shouted louder. So that's exactly what happened and now I have fixed everything and I am still alive.

Zoe Efstathiou

Illustration by Katie Wood

R.I.P. Eva McKell

Who was dearly loved and is regarded as a saint.
She was epic.

A white light flickered at the end of the tunnel. I put both hands before me and began to crawl. Wind kissed my cheek. A whirring noise grew in my ear. Something pulled me forward

... what happened next?

I was blinded by a harsh light. All I could think about was that there was no oxygen. A mysterious force summoned me from the tunnel. Still no air. My head felt a strength forcing it inwards as my vision blurred. I tried to wriggle back into the tube but I felt paralysed. I couldn't see. Still no air. A moment of calm washed over me before I felt my head tear away from my neck.

Eva McKell

All Hope Disappears

A white light flickered at the end of the tunnel. I put both hands before me and began to crawl. Wind kissed my cheek. A whirring noise grew in my ear. Something pulled me forward

... what happened next?

I was in the year 911 AD – when the Vikings were around. I looked down and saw myself wearing a toga and sandals with a silver metallic helmet perched uneasily on my head. Clutching a spear with my right hand and a shield with the other, I began to meander around this mysterious place. Nimble and ancient trees surrounded me as if I was a target for the kill. A bright, vibrant rainbow hovered above me. All seemed peaceful until ...

A flash of thumping lightning crackled high above me.

I felt electrocuted.

It was the Hammer of Thor!

Immediately, a gargantuan rainstorm crashed down on me through the howling wind. The awful weather was bullying me, showing no mercy. Frantically I sprinted in my saturated garments towards the nearest shelter within my view. Then my hope of finding shelter disappeared as I collided with a tough, muscular and large man – probably a warrior.

Story and illustration by Liam Fife

*A*bsolutely
Awesome
Adventure *of a*
Lifetime

Illustration by James Baldwin

Where would you go if you had the chance to go anywhere in the world? Would you travel to space or a jungle or the centre of the Earth? The next few stories are all about adventures from children's imaginations. They are leaping out of the page, pleading with you to read them! What are you waiting for?

Jon Parr

Are you OK, Pearl?

by Elodie Martin

There I was, sitting on a plane, looking out at the white fluffy clouds when all of a sudden my parents turn to me and say:

'Would you like a cookie?' I said: 'No thanks. I'm going to join my friends, Pearl and Amy, who are on the plane too.' 'OK,' said Mum. 'What are you going to do?' 'I'm going to jump off the plane onto a tree below in the rain forest!' I told her. 'But, Elodie, isn't that dangerous?' 'Not when you have a parachute!' I laughed and got out of my chair and walked off to where Amy and Pearl were putting their parachutes on. 'I've got my parachute. Do you have yours?' I said. 'Yes,' said Amy and Pearl together. Then we went over to the door. Pearl said: 'I hope we break the record of the youngest children to jump out of a plane 1000 meters high!' 'Yes, I hope so too!' I said. 'And me!' said Amy. 'We'd be famous,' she added. 'So which trees should we aim for?' I asked. 'How about that cluster of trees down there?' said Pearl. 'Yes, that would be safe,' said Amy. 'I agree too.' I said: 'Remember we have special permission from the pilot.' 'OK, we should be right over the trees now,' said Pearl, putting her hand on the handle. 'This is going to be cold,' said Amy.

When we got down there we looked at Pearl's leg and saw that it was floppy from half way down her shin.

'We need to make a stretcher or a bandage or something so that Pearl doesn't have to walk,' said Amy.

We started to make a stretcher for Pearl. We pulled vines and long branches from the trees. It took us ages to cut up the thick branches with our small, rusty, blunt pocket knife. When we had cut the branches, we used the pocket knife to cut up the vines until they were a centimetre thin. We tied the vines together until we had a massive green sheet. We tied the sheet to the branches that we'd collected earlier and put Pearl onto our woody stretcher, then started to carry her to the nearest village. We'd

Illustration by Ruby Aulman

made our stretcher really big so that three of us could fit onto it. We tied it between trees and slept on it because the journey was so long.

Elodie Martin

Escape

I was breathless, running through the jungle. I could hear my pursuers' footsteps gaining on me as I darted as quickly as a cheetah. I kept side stepping around trees, hoping to buy myself some time, but it did nothing to help me escape.

Suddenly I saw my escape! I leapt on the vine and swung up onto a huge tree. I taunted and jeered at the animal that was leaping up at the tree. I heard a growl coming from behind me on my branch. I said: 'You are right behind me, aren't you?' I dived into the undergrowth once again leaping on vines. My clothes were ripped but I still escaped.

James Baldwin

A Very Active Volcano

(writing prompt) **There I was, sitting on a plane, looking out at the white fluffy clouds when all of a sudden my parents turned to me and said:**

(writing begins)

'The driver's been murdered! The plane's going to crash!'

'Can't get any worse,' I said.

'Yes it can,' said my father. 'The plane's going to fall into an active volcano. The plane fell into the volcano and everybody died, even me. At least I had an adventure before I died.

The End

Arlo Freer

Aaaarrrrgggg!

(writing prompt) **There I was, sitting on a plane, looking out at the white fluffy clouds when all of a sudden my parents turned to me and said:**

(writing begins)

'Now we need to jump out of the plane!' 'What?' I cried out. 'We can't. No way!' And they shoved me out. I knew it was going to happen, just at the wrong time as I landed in a volcano well –

aaaaaaaaaaaaaaaaaaaaaarrrrrrrrrrrrrrrr rrrrrrggggggggggggggggg.

The End

Robert Parr

The Dancing Water Bottle Adventures

'Miss Water Bottle, will you marry me?' said Mr. Water Bottle.

'Yes,' said Miss Water Bottle.'

Miss Water Bottle,
illustration by Caity Cumner

'Now, darling. I've got to go the army.

I hope I see you soon ...'

'But I wish I could see you, Mr. Water Bottle.'

They got married and then Mr. Water Bottle went to the army. When he had a day off he went back home as quick as he could. When he got there, Mrs. Water Bottle made an announcement: 'I am pregnant. Here's one coming now!'

Just as she said it, a baby bottle dropped out of her.

'Ooooo,' she carried on. 'And here's another one.' That's when the second one popped out. After that they all went to bed but the baby water bottles woke up and went to space with Tim Peake.

Mr. and Mrs. Water Bottle woke up and couldn't find the babies. They worked out that the babies liked space and that they were probably with Tim Peake. So they went into his rocket and Mr.

Water Bottle said to the astronaut:

'I'm so excited that I've brought the whole house with me so that we can live with you in space.'

'Mrs. Water Bottle,' Mr. Water Bottle said, suddenly noticing his wife. 'Stop kissing Tim Peake this minute or I'll take you home and leave the kids up here.'

To be continued ...

Amelia Barwick, Naia Boyes & Caity Cumner

Mr. Water Bottle, illustration by Amelia Barwick

Inspiration for the Water Bottle Story

We always have a collection of water bottles on our tables, so we thought it would be fun to make them **come to life** and have awesome adventures.

Naia Boyes

To the Centre of the Earth

Once I planned to go on an adventure. I was going to go to the centre of the Earth on my own. I was very nervous. I was very angry that none of my family volunteered. They don't understand how very nervous I felt. I went to see how the hole that my drill was digging was getting on. (I had to dig a hole so I could get to the centre of the Earth. How else would I get there?)

Unfortunately the drill had gone too deep and the end had got melted by lava. 'That's deep enough,' I thought. So I got my climbing gear on and went down the hole.

The hole was very lonely and cold.

Arlo Freer

The Unexpected

(writing prompt) My parents turned to me and said: 'Get in! Now!'

Clawing my way into the helicopter, the blades turning rapidly, it bounced off the ground into the air and I began gliding through the clear sky. I observed the glorious views of the voluminous mountains and admired the animals staring up in wonder at the helicopter, adventuring relentlessly.

Approaching the glacier on the summit of the mountain, staring into the mouth of an ominous cave, we landed and I stepped into the abyss. The clouds faded away from the sky. Slowly, I approached the gloomy, creepy and gleaming cave. I stepped into the cave ...

The cave had scurrying noises and I was soon encaged by an awful, hollow sound echoing through the caves. Pushing my lantern forward into the darkness, like illuminating a black wall with light, I heard a growl which evolved into a group of echoing howls. Shining the lantern close to the source of the noise, the wolves' eyes glowed like flickering lights, blazing.

Getting chased by a cluster of hungry wolves as the mountain jolted, everything was unstable. A boulder obliterated the wolf pack. Only three bloodthirsty wolves remained. Their paws tighten, leaving scratches on the large boulder that crushed their tribe. My jaw was clenching, fear took control of my face. The wolves were silenced, for a moment. Suddenly, one leaped on me, his teeth painted red by his previous prey. With the wolf snapping at my neck, I released my knife deep into his calf. His warm blood trickled on my fingers. Fortunately, the other two scattered in the darkness, aimless.

Adventuring any further would be suicidal. The deadly wolves drove me in different directions. I was lost. Where were my parents? Scared, I moved towards the fog. I saw a glow. A gust of cold fresh air swirled around me.

A clap of thunder shook the mountain. I ran ...

If the avalanche reached the cave before I got out, I would die. I dashed. Focused forward. The rumbling of the snow echoed through the frozen cave where nightmares formed. I shot out as the snow ate me, hoping I wouldn't die, this close. Clawing my way through the frozen water, I felt a hand, warm and frail. It pulled me out of the heavy layers of white.

It was the pilot.   *Liam Fife*

The Amazon Adventure

(writing prompt) **There I was, sitting on a plane, looking out at the white fluffy clouds when all of a sudden my parents turned to me and said:**

"Quick! Put this parachute on. We're going to crash! Jump out of the plane!" "Geronimo," I said and I landed on the floor of the Amazon. Once I untangled myself I went hunting for food. When I was deep in the jungle, I suddenly saw a huge weird statue and spotted a weird symbol. I pushed the weird symbol and then a secret passageway came wide open and I went inside it. I got knocked out then woke up and found myself in a strange temple.

When I awoke in the temple I was surrounded by Indians. The Indians searched me. All they found was an orange pistol and lots and lots of bullets and three sandwiches. Then they took me to the prison ... I was in prison for a year. After a while I decided to look around the prison ... Looking, I found a knife so I started cutting my way out. Soon enough I was out of the prison. Searching for my backpack ... I escaped to the Amazon far, far away from the Indian campsite, then I heard a noise.

Suddenly an arrow shot towards me but missed, then I saw the Indians. I started shooting the Indians. More Indians were coming so I decided to make a run for it but as I ran, arrows were aiming for my head. The Indians wouldn't stop firing at me. Eventually I lost them and set up camp.

I started wishing in bed that I had never jumped out of the plane. I went to sleep. When I woke up and got out of my tent, I found there were footsteps there. There were about twenty footsteps that were about size five – my mum's size. I followed the footsteps and eventually they ended at a plane. I heard something, so I got my gun out but it was my mum.

My mum said "Get in the plane!" So I got in the plane and put my seatbelt on and we took off.

Finlay Denton

Underwater Expedition

By William Twining

(writing prompt) **There I was, sitting on a plane, looking out at the white fluffy clouds when all of a sudden my parents turned to me and said:**

"Go on, go and explore the world!"

I was wearing a swimsuit, a snorkel and some flippers. I waddled over to an emergency exit. Worry and wonder were jumbled up inside me like the alphabet in completely the wrong order. Like the flushing of a toilet, my stomach began to swirl creating an uneasy feeling in my body. I breathed a massive, massive, massive, massive breath and waved a potential farewell to my parents. Unsure about this so called 'adventure', I squeezed my eyes shut and stepped out of the plane. Fearful of this life-risking experience, I brace myself for the end of this perilous fall and wonder what awaits me.

SPLASH!!!

Immediately a huge mouthful of seawater filled up my mouth. Grimacing, I spat it out in disgust, already opening my mouth as I entered the ocean. Then my brain whirred into action and I focused on my surroundings. Gob-smacked, I stared in awe at the amazing sight before me. Thousands of bright, vibrant and colourful little fish swam beautifully in the shimmering sea. Their small delicate tails swished gently, creating tiny bubbles which floated aimlessly around this huge ocean. I tried to swim through all the fish, but there were just too many. Frustrated, I thought about how else I could get past them. Can't go left. Can't go right. Where else could I go? Under! Thinking this must be the only way to pass these little creatures, I dived down underneath them and swam through the empty water. At last! Delighted that I got past the fish, I

continued on my unexplored journey through this fabulous place. As time passed, night came closer and I began to search for somewhere to sleep. Casually, I surveyed my surroundings hoping to find a place suitable for me.

WHOOSH!

Instantaneously, a polar gush of water trickled up my spine like when you've got the nerves. Although it travelled quite quickly, I just could just spot a smooth stingray. Its massive wings flapped up and down swiftly and glided through calm water. Astounded, I stared in awe at the magnificent sea creature. I focused on my mission – to find somewhere to sleep.

Achieving my objective was not easy because I had to avoid this careless creature as well as finding somewhere decent for the night. Then all of a sudden, it rushed past me – its tail just millimetres away from hitting me. I realised I only had one chance to free *myself from this unhelpful catastrophe. I took a huge breath and went for it. As I swam through the water I squeezed my eyes tightly …*

I felt nothing. I knew what that meant. I had conquered the unhelpful! Triumphant, I knew that I had to escape quickly in case the stingray was back again.

Slowly but noticeably I began to tire. My feet began to flap instead of kick. I was never going to have any success in finding a place to sleep.

Just as I was about to give up, my dreary eyes spotted a small netted hammock swaying gently in the peaceful water. An optimistic spirit replaced the old negative one. I was like a new robot just starting a new life.

Ecstatic, I glided through the ocean towards the lonely, ancient piece of

furniture. Because I was exhausted, I just lolloped onto the hammock. I breathed my final breath before I closed my eyes and began to sleep.

The next day was a new day. I was woken up by a joyful spirit. There's no time to waste, I thought. Eager to explore I began to swim and continue on my fabulous experience through this energetic sea life. I'd never been so thrilled in my life. Optimism filled my spirits.

As I looked ahead into the distance, I spied a glistening gleam of gold. Wondering where it came from, I headed towards the vibrant colour of gold expecting some kind of exquisite protection. As I neared the colour ....

... to be continued

William Twining

*U*nderground *Worlds*

At Putting Pen to Paper we made underground worlds for characters to live in, eg: Giggle World was created by Giggle Queen (that's me, Caitlin), Amelia and Caity. There was a great party underneath and everyone was giggling - of course.

Caitlin Willcocks

Illustration by Caity Cumner

Writing Prompts: Underground Worlds

My name is *Hammer T. Mole.*

One day I was sitting in my underground world when, all of a sudden, soil fell on my head. I looked up. You'll never guess who I saw coming down from the ceiling! I began to shout: *"Hi!"*

My visitor replied: *"I'm Cheese Bob Nugget."*

Then my best friend tapped me on the shoulder. His face said it all: *"Dude, he*

looks like he was born in a pizza van and I like it."

We ran away, leaving our visitor screaming behind us: *"They want to drink your blood!"*

Story and illustration by Niall Cornelius

Underground Worlds: What is this?

This '*animal*' found its way to Putting Pen to Paper. What kind of animal do you think it is and how did it get here? Go to page 160 to find the answer.

*Illustration of **Big Dave** by James Baldwin &*
Robert Parr

My name is **Clarabella.**

One day I was sitting in my underground world when, all of a sudden, soil fell on my head. I looked up. You'll never guess who I saw coming down from the ceiling! I began to shout: *"Sir Giggleton, mad scientist. Blob is attacking."*

My visitor replied: *"My name is Blob. I come in peace. Well ... not quite."*

Then my best friend tapped me on the shoulder. His face said it all: *"Blob is attacking. He was meant to defend Fairytopia. I never should've made him."*

We ran away, leaving our visitor screaming behind us: *"Fairytopia tonight will be destroyed. I hate you all."*

Caitlin O'Boyle

My name is *Slime the Snail.*

One day I was sitting in my underground world when, all of a sudden, soil fell on my head. I looked up. You'll never guess who I saw coming down from the ceiling! I began to shout: *"Blob! It's the Blob! Blob is here to destroy us!"*

Blob replied: *"I'm here to destroy you!"*

Then Freaky Spoon tapped me on the shoulder. His face said it all: *"Slime, this is no joke. You need to run."*

"But I can't run. I'm a snail that goes slowly …"

Freaky Spoon ran away leaving me all on my own to defeat Blob.

To be continued ...

Illustration by Daisy Redding

Underground is a *DIRTY* Place ...

Underground is a **dirty** place, but in our world you can have an underground party and there are leaves you can sleep on with lots of tunnels you can squeeze through where you can find **insects** and **skeleton bones**.

It is **dark,** but we have torch lights and a furnace and you can eat lots of different types of fish and there are **ropes** to climb up the steep **tunnels**.

There are balloons for the party and banners saying '**UNDERGROUND PARTY**' with a radio to record fun music.

You can discover new places to squeeze through and small gaps for fish and bones. It is such fun to find bones - but be careful not to get bitten.

Story and illustration by James Baldwin

The Old Man, the Spider and the Shark

One day underground, on a crisp winter's day, there suddenly appeared, out of the mist, a spooky old house. There were cobwebs and spiders everywhere.

In the old house, there lived an old man. He looked as old as the house itself. The old man wandered along the dusty old street, wondering what he would do today, but at that very moment he came across a spider. He decided it might taste nice. He wanted to eat it, but the spider quickly disappeared.

The spider wanted a small bite of a shark so he went to the beach on holiday. There he was about to eat a shark when the shark decided to eat the spider first.

The enzymes in the shark's saliva broke down the spider in the shark's small intestine and it went down into the large intestine. After twelve hours, the spider went into the bowel of the shark and came out the other end.

Eva McKell, Maiya O'Boyle, Ellie Cumner & Caitlin O'Boyle

*P*erfect Poems &

Puzzling Puzzles

You have never read anything as good as children's poems. This chapter is filled with rhythm and rhyme so prepare to be amazed with poems that will knock your socks off! Get ready to be blasted with poems.

Ruby Aulman

Slug

Slow, slow slug,
wriggling along the ground,
you're not much of a bug,
eating leaves without a sound.

Elodie Martin

Buttercup

Buttercup, buttercup,

amongst the greenery,

with shiny yellow petals,

next to a peony.

Elodie Martin

Illustration by Lorien Boyes

The Fish

I swim around in the deep, deep sea,

I'm as scaly as can be.

I have one fin and two flippers.

I don't have any feet to wear slippers.

Maiya O'Boyle

What am I?

I am transparent
but am not.
We are here.
Sometimes you put
transparent
things over me.

Answer: We are eyeballs.

James Baldwin & Robert Parr

Poppy McPop

Once there was a guinea
pig named Poppy McPop,
he always hops all the
way to the top.

He eats and eats and eats
all day,

and always loves to come
out and play.

Shop, shop, shop all day,

carrots he likes to shop.

Ellie Cumner

Illustration by Edward Scott

In the Jungle

In the jungle I am the king
The others run away from anything.
I love the sun,
it's lots of fun.
But the rain is such a pain.
I am a big cat,
I make others go splat.

Robert Parr

What am I?
In the water I sail.

I could be a shark or a whale.

I go deep in the ocean.

I am fast, as fast as a fastness potion.

What am I?

Answer: I am a seahorse

Robert Parr

What am I?

I eat mice. I have big eyes. I can fly?

What am I?

Answer: I am an owl

Joshua Panes

What am I?

Darkness

I am everywhere;

in the sun.

Never the dark.

We shrink then grow

then disappear

for a long time.

This proves you

are never alone.

Answer: I am a shadow

James Baldwin & Robert Parr

We wrote the poem *Darkness* when we were matching quotes to books during the **Wicked Friendship** course. We saw this quote from Roald Dahl's '*Matilda*' and it inspired us to write our poem, **Darkness**: *"So Matilda's strong young mind continued to grow, nurtured by the voices of all those authors who had sent their books out into the world like ships on the sea. These books gave Matilda a hopeful and comforting message: **you are not alone**.'* ('*Matilda*' by Roald Dahl, first published in 1988)

What am I?

I chase and chase my prey until they end
their day. They lose all their puff and turn to
fluff when I eat them up. What am I?
Answer: I am a bull shark

Joshua Panes

What am I?

I swing from tree to tree
With bananas. I say "Yippee!"
A brown tail stretches behind me,
but I'm still very happy. What am I?
Answer: I am a monkey

Liam Fife

What am I?

I live in salt water. I am green. I have
sharp teeth. What am I?
Answer: I am a saltwater crocodile

Joshua Panes

CREATURE

If I could make a creature it will be

ten feet long and live up a tree.

Small, soft paws like an elf,

it makes a platform like a shelf.

Jade green tail full of venom.

One small touch and you'll be in heaven.

Jet black fur like the night air

Tail colourless, without hair.

It prowls around in the night.

It is evil and will get in a fight.

And now finally to name the beast -

he is called the Fan-gest.

James Baldwin

FRIENDS

Friendship

Rainbow

Imagination

Excited

Nice

Dreams

Secrets

Orla Morrison & Anna Styles

Illustration by Anna Styles

The Hat of Honour

Once there was a fish called Clive and he was on a quest to find a ring. On the way to find a ring, he found a discarded gas mask box. Inside the box there were strange eye-fingery things. Clive swam on and got caught in a red scarf. But luckily near Clive there was a pointer-stick with which he untangled himself. Soon Clive found a box with the ring that he wanted in it. When he got home and showed the ring, his friends gave him a hat of honour.

Caitlin O'Boyle

*F*antastic Flash Writing

Sometimes we play the Prop Game. The Prop Game is where there are loads of objects in a prop bag, AKA a bin bag, and you pick out an object. The aim of the game is to write a story including the props. Caitlin picked out a ring, gas mask box, strange eye-finger toys, a red scarf, a pointer stick, a box and a hat! Very hard, but she did it! And here's the story, *The Hat of Honour*, opposite this very page.

Orla Morrison

Super Moon Rising

The moon was rising quickly. Evil
filled the air. The light flooded the
fairy's hide-out. Passing back and
forth, the citizens of Fairytopia ...
They knew the enemy, Blob,
would be attacking.
Suddenly, Blob appeared in the
moonlight.
'Prepare to be destroyed!'
groaned Blob.
'I think not!' yelled Becky, riding
Piglet.
One swish with her sword and she
had defeated Blob.

Ellie Cumner

The Squirrel

I was walking through the
park when suddenly a squirrel
said to me:
'Oi! You there!'
Then I said: 'What?'
'Help me off this fence.'
'No.'
'I'll give you a chocolate if you
do,' he called back.

Ruby Aulman

*This piece of writing was inspired by a
picture of a squirrel sitting on an iron fence
in a park. It looked as if it was saying
something ...like, 'Oi! You there!'*

Super Moon Rising

As the sun beam hit the moon, it reflected with a giant glow. All the monsters were called out from their hiding place and the glow of the moon flooded their underground world. It burned the roof. The scissors cut the cellotape. The giant Lemon of Doom fell down causing an earthquake which woke up the Evil Hand. Evil Hand strangled everyone. Then he bit the cellotape which started swinging the spoon and got cut by scissors which landed on a pressure plate which made the blobs fall through the roof so zombies and monsters can get in and they have a fight. They fall on another pressure plate which sets off TNT which defeats all the monsters but it also blows up the world.

Apparently the blobs landed on another planet and will seek their revenge.

James Baldwin & Jon Parr

Illustration by Caity Cumner

Farts

IT'S GONNA

BLOW!

ARE YOU READY ... to turn the pages ... to see stories that will blow you a w a y? Are you ready to discover

TURN THE PAGE ...

(Oh, the smell, the smell ...)

Arlo Freer

Parp-zania

I was captured by an alien life force and taken to **Parp-zania**, the Land of Farts. A gas cloud collided with the fart-powered spaceship and caused it to fall into a volcano. PARP! I shot out and into a fart river. I passed out there ...

I woke up in a hospital. They were forcing fart gas into my brain. When they saw I was awake they flushed me in a giant loo and I was in my room. Mum and Dad came in and farted. The house exploded. Turned out I was still in **Parp-zania**. I fell to the ground, went through it and woke up not knowing if it was a dream or not. My Dad made me pass out.

Jon Parr

The Blue Moon

There was a Super Moon rising. I'm so excited. It's not every day you get to see a Super Moon. It only happens every 500 years. Although I was excited, my sister Amy was not. There were myths that when the moon came up, monsters lurked.

One of my favourite myths was Blob who was known to lurk in the shadows, waiting to pounce. He destroyed everything. Until one day a brave, unknown hero killed Blob. The myth says that every Super Moon, Blob *strikes* ...

It is one of my favourite myths because it's got adventure in it. Something I've never had.

But finally it's happening and it's as bright as the sun and as blue as the sea!

I couldn't take my eyes off it.

Then I saw something. Something I thought I would never see ...

... it was Blob.

Maiya O'Boyle

Illustration by Caitlin O'Boyle

Weird & Wonderful Wildlife

Illustration by Amy Lucas

This chapter is spread with colourful stories with talking dogs as icing on the top. The real answer to nature's mysteries will be uncovered in this mind-blowing chapter. Be prepared: the truth is unpredictable.

Liam Fife

Some of our *own* wacky, weird and wonderful wildlife

Weird & Wonderful Wildlife

Ginger the Guinea Pig

Ginger the guinea pig went down into the town and bought some round carrots to eat for lunch. But when she went home she found out that she had forgotten her glasses so she put them back on. She took out the round carrots from the bag and found out they were oranges.

Ingrid Linge

Dye, Di, Dye, Dye ...

Miss Poppypiggle raced across the hall, screaming after her daughter. She was furious. Her daughter, however, was struggling to stand up, she was laughing so hard. Mrs. Poppypiggle ignored her son's screams as he attempted to wash green hair dye from his silky coat and slammed into her daughter, knocking her onto the floor. Despite the pain, her daughter refused to stop laughing as her brother furiously ran out of his room, hair bright green.

Eva McKell

Venelopy Meets a Mouse

by Alison Weideman

Venelopy is a poor guinea pig. She lives on her own and has never met anyone. Her home is a rubbish tip. When it gets cold, Venelopy hides in an old tin can. That is what she calls *home*.

One day she had a plan. She would leave her home and find a friend. The day she would do it would be the next day. When she woke up, she packed her bag to leave home. She put in food, drink, toys and bedding. She set off to find a beautiful, amazing fun friend.

It was a long, hard trip to get out of the rubbish tip. Venelopy kept on getting lost. She even got stuck in a bulldozer. She was relieved to be out of trouble so she carried on the journey.

She saw a board that said NEW YORK. That is when she found out she was in New

York City. New York was the place she hoped to be in. She knew she would find a friend with big, bubbly, bouncy ideas in New York.

She started to travel the world. One of the things she had to get past was a road. It was a very dangerous place for a young guinea pig to be. When it was time to get ready to cross, Venelopy looked to see if it was safe. She ran across the road just in time because a car was coming towards her.

On the other side of the road there was a dog. What would she do? She needed some help. So she went up to the dog. The dog said: "How can I help you?" Venelopy was amazed to see thatthe dog wanted to help her. "I need to get to the countryside,' replied Venelopy.

The dog took her to the beautiful countryside.

"Thank you for taking me," said Venelopy to the dog. "You're welcome," replied the dog in a gentle voice.

In the distance she saw Mr. Willy Wonka's Chocolate Factory! She was a big fan of Mr. Wonka and Mr. Wonka was a big fan of Venelopy. He had a big surprise for her: it was a mouse. Willy Wonka was coming in his elevator with Charlie, Grandpa Joe, Grandpa George, Grandma Josephine, Grandma Georgina and Charlie's mum and dad. They were all pleased to meet each other. Mr Wonka let Venelopy live with his pet mouse in his factory. Venelopy had plenty of food to eat and a friend to play with.

Venelopy was no longer a poor guinea pig.

Alison Weideman

BONGO THE JEWEL THIEF

This story is about a guinea pig. He is a robber. His name is Bongo. He tries to steal a gem. He has two friends, Tommy and Pop. Bongo tries to steal the great gem of Jupiter. He does it with robot trousers and a helmet on his head with a claw inside that grabs the gem. He gets caught and gets put in Zoo Jail.

Tommy and Pop get free tickets to sky dive into a pool with a policeman – into a Water Jail. The policemen are birds so they can fly out of the Water Jail but Tommy and Pop don't because they are seals.

Tom Panes

WHEN THE HUNTERS CAME

One step into the jungle and I was surrounded by animals. There were lions, tigers, monkeys and much more. I then said to the animals: 'I won't harm you.' The animals bit away their teeth and claws. The animals and I became good friends. We lived in a tree house in the jungle very happily. But one day that all changed. Hunters came and destroyed our home. The animals thought I was with the hunters.

Caity Cumner

Unpopped Popcorn

Icepop the popping guinea pig went down the street to the supermarket to get some popcorn for tea. Icepop went to the shop and found there was no popcorn. She was devastated. She hoped she could stock up for the whole month so she went to the shop next door. It was Sadie and Dobbie's shop. It had popcorn! Yes, she couldn't believe her luck!

When she got home she went up to her hutch then opened the bag and found UNPOPPED POPCORN.

Caitlin O'Boyle

Illustration by Erin South

Writing Prompts

There was a massive thunderstorm and a lightning bolt shot from the sky and lit up ... **a bottle of brown nuts that were falling from the sky. Quickly, mad monkeys invaded.**

The animals had to run for cover. They ... **accidentally ran into a huge pet shop. The angry pet shop owner threw tasty dog biscuits at the mad monkeys and they exploded.**

The next thing that happened was a huge thunderclap ... **and the birds went crazy ... the parrots, the budgerigars ... and knocked out the monkeys again.**

Did you know animals are scared by ... **radishes, because they think the red bits mean death, laser-shooting radishes.**

They found a safe place to hide from the storm with ... **bird food for the birds, the budgerigars and the parrots.**

Robert Parr, Jon Parr, Joshua Panes & Tom Panes

One of our tasks was to be given **a list of words** and make a story or write a description, using them. Here are some examples using the following words ...

Jon Parr

Rough  *fishy*

dirty golden

The tiger was rough and dirty. It smelt fishy and it was golden. It found gold. The gold was slimy and hard and rough. It felt smooth. The tiger found grey sand.

Tom Panes

rough *smooth*

glistening **filthy**

crumbly

Made-up Creature Description

The dirty lava came out of a cow's shimmering tail. Its glitzin' body shimmered in the rough, smooth desert. A golden, cracky ball that is camouflaged shot from the grey sky. The thing was fishy because it was flaky and shelly. Then its delicate body revealed a slimy, fat body of scaly fish in a crumbly box. Suddenly, something **soft** ran away.

Jon Parr

All I Remember ...

"I hate having to keep scratching my head." I heard the person I had decided to plant my nit army in say. It was in a very warm place that had everything I ever wanted: BLOOD! The head had all the textures I had ever wanted in my house full of food: it was rough, smooth, scaly, glistening, crumbly and full of what I call golden larva. I called my army as we had just had a terrifying nit comb go through the hair. We all fled for our lives.

*We saw the **filthy** nit comb come through the hair. I was captured as soon as the comb laid eyes on me. I went into a trance so I stayed dead still. That is all I remember.*

Caitlin O'Boyle

*Buzz ... I am a fly. I **buzz** around and this is what I see ...*

... big and fat chickens, feathers galore, with green feathers shining in the sunlight. Their beaks are orange like an orange. Out of them comes hot lava so they can roast a chicken for Sunday lunch.

Joshua Panes

The Debate: The In or Out of Captivity Vote

My Campaign Speech ... I think that animals should stay in their natural habitat. If they come from a hot country, the animals will suffer in a colder climate. Also, their cages are smaller and there is not enough room to move around.

Let's take a tiger, for example. If they get given food instead of catching the prey themselves, they won't be able to catch food when they are released back into the wild.

For another example, an antelope. If there isn't enough space they will lose their speed. So when they are released into the wild, the big cats will catch them because of their loss of speed.

In conclusion, VOTE OUT.

THANK YOU. *Erin South*

The Debate: The In or Out of Captivity Vote

My Campaign Speech ... Do you want lots of wildlife to become extinct? Do you want massively reduced amounts of fantastic animals to admire at zoos? The obvious answer to both these questions is 'No'. Therefore, as a team, we should keep endangered species in captivity which will protect them much better than the dangerous wild. Furthermore, this will prevent hunters and poachers from destroying the lovely creatures' lives. Taking these endangered animals to safe zoos is a huge benefit and boost to their lives. We will provide them with all of the natural resources that they require to keep safe.

In conclusion, VOTE IN b**ecause** we have the care to protect them from danger. Also, we have got the quality of making this home as close to being exactly like their habitat in the wild. **THANK YOU.**

William Twining

Stupendous Speech and Dramatic Dialogue

This chapter is all about silly speech and dialogue. Be careful - the speech marks might jump out of the page. Read on to find out about our wonderful work on SPEECH.

Lorien Boyes

DINOSAURS

Narrator: A white light flickered at the end of the tunnel. The girls put both hands before them and began to crawl. Wind kissed their cheeks. A whirring noise grew in their ears. Something pulled Amelia forward.

Amelia and Caity crawl along the floor. Amelia is being pulled forward and she grabs onto Caity

Amelia: It's a dinosaur. I think we have gone into dinosaur times ...

Caity: Yeah! But what do we do?

Amelia: I don't know.

141

Narrator: They carefully walked past the dinosaurs.

Caity and Amelia walk carefully

Caity: Why aren't they trying to eat us?

Amelia: Because they are herbivores.

Caity: Look! There's that tunnel we came through.

Narrator: So the girls tried to get to the tunnel.

Amelia: Finally. We are at the Tunnel.

Caity: Let's go home now.

Amelia: Good idea!

Caity: You can come to my house for a sleepover.

Amelia Barwick & Caity Cumner

Lord of the Gold

Jon: Robert, I found this map to some gold.

Robert: Well, what are we waiting for? Go!

James: Perfect. I will get them for once.

Jon: Looks like we need to find a chest underground.

Robert: You have the map upside down!

Robert slaps his own head and then puts his head in both hands

Jon: Oh! It must be in the sky then?

Robert: Let's climb Spinnaker Tower then.

James: I will set fire to the rope and it will Break.

Robert: EPIC!

Jon: Arrrrrrrrrrr!

Jon falls down from the tower, his legs kicking in the air

Robert: Seriously, who put a trampoline here?

Jon lands on a trampoline and bounces back up into the air

Jon: I am alive.

James: Not for long. Bong!

James bops them on the head with a bat

Jon Parr, Robert Parr & James Baldwin

Illustrations (top left to bottom right) by Maia O'Boyle, Jemima Butler & Liv Fairhead

The Explorers of Oz!

by Ruby Aulman, Elodie Martin, Orla Morrison, Anna Styles
& Caitlin Willcocks

Illustration by Caity Cumner

Narrator: I would like to introduce the *Explorers of Oz:* We have: 1st the worst, 2nd the best, 3rd is the one with the hairy chest, 4th from the North and 5th is the one with the powerful gun.

1st the worst: Oh dear, I'm lost now. I'll never get home.

(jumps out of a bush)

2nd the best: You'll always be able to find your way home with me and my snow leopard, Cloudy. I'm the best explorer.

Narrator: When they move on to find the powerful Explorer of Oz to help 1st home, they find another explorer.

(other explorer jumps out of a bush)

3rd is the one with the hairy chest: Hello. I'm 3rd! I can also help you get home!

Narrator: They started walking on again when out popped another explorer. How many explorers can there be in this story?

(another explorer jumps out of a bush)

4th is the North: 4th from the North at your service! How can I help you?

1st the worst: We are trying to find the Explorer of Oz. Do you know the way?

4th is the North: I dooooo ... Go through the Evergreen Forest, turn right, go up the Snowy Mountain, go down the other side of the Snowy Mountain and turn left.

Narrator: Off the explorers go and after an eternity they rolled down the Snowy Mountain, turned left and saw the Explorer of Oz. She is in a grumpy mood.

5th is the one with the powerful gun: (grumpy voice) What do you want?

All: We want to go home and we don't know the way. Can you help us?

5th is the one with the powerful gun: Go to the Land of Lords. In a huge room you will find a huge mirror on a glass wall. Then make your wish …

Narrator: They start walking to the Land of Lords.

2nd the best: Hey, look! There's a mirror on a glass wall. It must be it.

3rd is the one with the hairy chest: Let's go and get it.

Narrator: They go to get the mirror and make their wish. Suddenly they find themselves in a plane coming home.

1st the worst: The mirror got us back.

3rd is the one with the hairy chest: Yay!

2nd the best: We're home.

4th is the North: We made it.

5th is the one with the powerful gun: Finally, peace.

All: Wow! That really *was* an adventure.

The End

Ruby Aulman, Elodie Martin, Orla Morrison, Anna Styles
& Caitlin Willcocks

Chapter 2: Adventure but with the Parent's Permission

Mr. Waterbottle: Let's go on an adventure with a friend of mine.

They all go

Baby MW: Oh, look! A bat.
Baby OC: Let's keep him.
Mrs. Waterbottle: No. It's too dangerous.
Mr. Waterbottle: Let's keep this boot.
Baby MW: Help! Wa, wa, wa ...
Baggy: I'll help you.

Baggy helps Maby MW

Baby OC: I'm tired. Let's go home.
Mrs. Waterbottle: Which way's home, Amelia?
Mr. Waterbottle: We've lost a child.
Baggy: Don't worry. I've got him.

They arrive home

Baby OC: Ah! The kitchen is the best place to be.

Caity Cumner

Wardrobe Adventures

Illustration by Maiya O'Boyle

Anna & Lorien:	There once were two explorers called Amelia and Naia.
Amelia:	Shall we go on an adventure?
Naia:	Where shall we go?'
Anna:	Step into the wardrobe.
Lorien:	You will find yourself in a rainforest.
Anna & Lorien:	They stepped in and it was black.
Amelia:	It's really dark.

(Amelia falls over)

| Naia: | I have a light switch. |
| Amelia: | I've found it. I've found it. |

Naia: That's not a light switch, it's a
           monkey.
Anna: I've got some advice.

Anna &
Lorien: *(Looking at each other)*
           RUN!
Amelia &
Naia: WHY?
Anna: Quickly, they ran as fast as
           they could. The monkey
           stared at them while they
           stumbled to a tree.
Amelia: Let's climb up the tree.
Naia: There's our wardrobe!
Anna &
Lorien: They went in.

Amelia: What an adventure!

All four: *The end.*

Amelia Barwick, Anna Styles, Naia & Lorien Boyes

Liam's Krazy Kool Krossword

Across

2 What's the first name of the person who created Putting Pen to Paper?

3 Is this book AWESOME?

4 This book is blihsPude

5 The 8th word in the title of Vol. 1

8 A big book by small _____

9 The Big Putting Pen to Paper _____ Doodah Book

Down

1 What's the colour of the front cover (Vol 1) ?

3 nguYo uAthros

6 A piece of text usually written on the back of the book

7 How many books will there be by the end of this second year of PP2P?

*K*razy Kool Krossword

The crossword across the page was created by techno wizard, Liam Fife, and used as a class activity. Can you find the answers? Go to page 160 to check them out and see how many you got right.

swiftly **BIG**

fishy slimy

rough *smooth*ly

spiral *dirty* skinny

glistening

larva **scaly**

smooth

*A*mazing *Adjectives*

Adjectives are words that describe a noun, so flick through the pages and see our brilliant adjectives. How many of the ADJECTIVES across the page can YOU use?

SKINNY SNAIL

It was all running smoothly at Putting Pen to Paper when a rough shelled garden snail came in dragging a spiral, delicate wasp nest. The snail left a dirty, glistening, skinny trail following swiftly behind him. After a while we found out that he was heading towards the old, grey, creaky snail shells. But heads turned towards a gold, fishy, scaly, golden, smooth goldfish in the corner. The fish tail turned in the water and caused waves in children's minds. The larva-coloured camouflaged goldfish took the spotlight away from the skinny snail.

Did you enjoy my **big** story?

Lorien Boyes

*N*aughty
Nouns

What is a noun? A noun is the name of something, such as a shoe (an object), a person (me) or a place (like the place we go to for Putting Pen to Paper).

Nouns can be described as 'naughty' because we were looking at alliteration. We could have used

'Normal' but we thought that

'Naughty' was a much better word.

Lorien Boyes

Anthropomorphism

It's a brilliant word but what does it mean? Beatrix Potter's character, Peter Rabbit, is *anthropomorphic*, meaning he is an animal with human characteristics. *Anthropomorphism* is the NOUN. If you see a long word, don't freak out. Break it down, here, like this:

An-thro – po-morph-ism

Think of it like a bicycle chain or a bracelet: to make a whole chain or bracelet you need different pieces that are linked together. So, here's a challenge: look at the word

anthropomorphism

and see how many words are hidden inside it, like **ant** or **mop**. Are there four, fourteen or forty? Are there more? Go to page 161 for some of the answers.

V ibrant Verbs

Recently at Putting Pen to Paper we have been looking at verbs. This chapter is stuffed with some of the hard work we have put into getting those verbs right.

Ruby Aulman

What is a Verb?

Well, a verb is an ACTION word. Every sentence should have a verb in it. Test your brains and circle the verbs in the list over the page. It's full of all kinds of stuff (answers on page 161).

hover-legs	MedusI	moon cheese
alien	to defeat	soft
pupils	eyelet	nose
Groblet	shrivelled	green
spaceship	uni-brow	squidgy
Blob	cosmos	Swatty Spotty
see-through	hero	Bloberina
evil	flying	lasers
ballerina	UFO	experimenting
smelly	slimy	planet
aviator	crashing	galaxies
shooting	scientist	travelling
asteroid	landing	sparkly
zooming	mad	Blob Junior

*E*pic Editing

We edit because something might not make sense or we might have repeated a word too many times (*we even edited this paragraph before we wrote it up in neat*). That's EPIC!

Also, when we think our work is done, we go back to it to see if it needs improving. That's editing.

By the extra-ordinary editors,
Anna Styles & Orla Morrison

Illustration by Orla Morrison

Answers

Underground Worlds: what is this? *(from page 97)* It wasn't an *animal* at all but the combination of a coat and a furry hat!

Liam's Kool Krossword Answers *(from pages 150/151)*

Across: 2 SARAH; 3 YES; 4 PUBLISHED; 5 DOODAH; 8 CHILDREN; 9 BONKERS

Down: 1 ORANGE; 3 YOUNG AUTHORS; 6 BLURB; 7 TWO

Anthropomorphism : just how many words **could** you find

hidden in there on page 156? Here are *SOME* of the words our top word-finder, William Twining, was able to find.

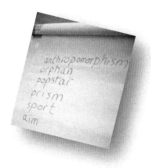

soon, **mat**, moan, **star**, art, **opt**, popstar, **sat**, sit, **soap**, mop, **shirt**, short, **prism**, host, **port**, sport, **orphan**, son, **pit,** into, **no**, to, **aim**, stain, **mash,** than, **moon**, storm, **room**, strip, **oar**, most, **strap,** is, **spot**, hoop, **horn**, poor, **thin**, pin, **saint**, hip, **moor**, pom-pom, **mist**, pant, **hit**, hat, **trash,** root

Vibrant Verbs : how many verbs did you find on page 158? Did you get these?

shooting	shrivelled	landing
zooming	experimenting	flying
to defeat	crashing	travelling

What are **verbs** again? Verbs are words of ***ACTION***.

Absolutely Awesome Adventure of a Lifetime: We Liked These Great Words and Word Combinations ...

'bridge of pens' : Caitlin O'Boyle

'youngest to jump out'; 'cluster of trees';
'roaring wind' : Elodie Martin

'entangled'; 'secret passageway':

Finlay Denton

'parachuting aeroplane'; 'conservation camp';
'talking monkeys' : Anna Styles

'flatlands'; 'combat chief'; 'parody';
'pro-laugh' : Liv Fairhead

'waddled'; 'like the flushing of a toilet';
'potential farewell' : William Twining

Go back to pages 75 to 94 to revisit the stories.

*W*hat We Like About

Putting Pen to Paper ('PP2P')

'... getting ideas and writing stories.'

Finlay Denton

'**Creating** anything.'

Ellie Cumner

'Reading out and acting.'

Robert Parr

'... writing whilst making new friends.'

Caitlin O'Boyle

'Everything, but especially the **scriptwriting** and **drama**.'

Caitlin Willcocks

' ... making animal homes ...'

James Baldwin

'... making new friends ...'   *Orla Morrison*

'Everything.'   *Liam Fife*

'... the exciting atmosphere ...'

Ingrid Linge

'I really enjoyed writing stories and showing them to Sarah or Kate.'

Liv Fairhead

'Literally everything, especially 'being a criminal''

Erin South

'Showcasing my work.'

Ruby Aulman

*P*utting *P*en to *P*aper is also about ...

... helping others ...

... it's about mentoring ...

... it's about working together ...

... it's about friendship ...

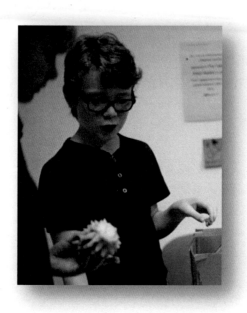

... it's also about being happy and having fun.

If you are aged 7-11 and would like to find a place where you can write or become a young author out of school, come and talk to us or download an Application Form from the following link:

http://www.madaboutsnailbooks.com/pen-to-paper-courses/

and return it to the address at the bottom of the form. If you are aged 11 (+) and would like to join as a Young Mentor, gain experience for the Duke of Edinburgh Scheme or you are a college student looking for a general volunteering opportunity, please contact Sarah Lucas on 01420 587351 or send an e-mail to:
sarah@madaboutsnailbooks.com

NOTE

Thanks to all these companies, organisations and people for helping to make this book happen.

THANK YOU!

East Hampshire District Council's Community Initiative Fund

Alton Beer Festival
Chief Commissioner of the Grammar Police, Christopher Sparkes *('Grammar Without Groans')*
DG Design and Print
Joanna Short Photography
Madaboutsnailbooks (masb)
Treloar Print
... and all The Maltings Centre staff who make us feel so welcome.

The Team
Sarah Lucas & Kate Collins
Volunteers – Emily Hillan & Mark Magapantay
Duke of Edinburgh Scheme Student: George Lucas
Resources (Support): Rachel Swatton
Creative Support: Amy Lucas
Young Mentors: William Egginton & William Osborne